A Greater Force Than Failure

<><><><><><><><><><><><><><><><><><><><><><><><><><><><><><><><><><>

Intentional Time with God

<><><><><><><><><><><><><><><><><><><><><><><><><><><><><><><><><><><>

CREATED BY

ADRIENNE TOWNSEND BENTON

May God continue
to really bless you always

love
Chaplain Benton

THIS JOURNAL BELONGS TO

_____

_____

CONTENTS

DEDICATION

*To God—My heart is grateful,
and I give this journal back to You.*

*To my amazing and supportive husband Theron
Benton—I love you and let's keep impacting
the world together.*

*To my family and faithful friends who have prayed with
me, supported, and sown into God's leading in my life—
this book is evidence of the answer to one amongst many
of your prayers.*

*To all lifelong faith learners and doers who, with an open
heart, are open right now to receiving.*

HOW TO USE THIS JOURNAL

Have you ever failed? Have you ever given your best effort, yet you still missed the mark? How did you feel after you tried and failed? Sad, rejected, discouraged? No one is perfect, so maybe, just maybe, you have even failed more than once? If you answered yes, don't worry…you are not alone.

This occurrence called *failure* is a universal human experience. What makes the difference is what you do with the failure—how you handle the failure and your perspective on moving forward from the failure again, and again, and yes again.

I have found that in life, my perspective, my pardon, my passion, and my pain all require that I have extraordinary intentional faith in order for me to move forward. I want to do more than just exist; with God's determination and strength, I want to persist. I want to do more than survive; with God's dedication and courage, I want to thrive.

What about you? Do you want to have intentional continuous faith in God? The faith that takes Him at His word and believes that He is for you?

The pages in this journal are here to walk with you on the journey where you recognize and employ Godly *faith* as the greater force than *fear* in your life. Fear = False Evidence Appearing Real. Remember, failures do not have to be fatal. You can recover!

In this journal I recommend that you honestly fill out the prompts and reflect. The motivational quotes and scripture verses that are sprinkled on each page are there for you to repeat to yourself, pray, and rebuild your thinking.

May God transform your mind, heart, and life. Now let's get started!

Faith. It's all about believing.

You don't know how it will happen. But you know it will.

~Anonymous

FOUR REASONS WHY YOU'LL LOVE A GREATER FORCE THAN FAILURE

1. The most intentional action you can do every day is to take time for you! We get so caught up in our busy lives, and it is time to replenish yourself with perspective and time to engage with God and yourself.

2. This is a journal for people who don't do journals. There is beauty that comes from trying a new activity. Let go of your worries and live in the moment. This journal is self-guided. No pressure on completing it by a certain time. Take your time and enjoy!

3. You will have a snapshot of your struggle of faith over your fears. What is holding you back from moving forward? Where do you want God to heal you so you do not make the same mistakes over and over again? What voices of failure and negativity is it time to refuse to listen to? The time is now. Know that you are not walking on this journey alone. Many people have prayed for you and are praying for you right now. Yes, as you are readying this, someone is praying for you.

4. Have a problem sticking to a commitment? Good. This journal is for you. Enjoy!

MY WHY

A Greater Force Than Failure

As I write this journal, I am forced to revisit my own life journey with failure. I am confronted with the fact that I have "failed" more times that I want to recall. Some of the failures were inconsequential. Light, momentary, private, and "no big deal." Then there were other ones. You know, the ones that were public, painful, and problematic. The failures that cause you to pause and stand still. The failures that opened the door for fear and let it reside.

When I tried to move on, do damage control, and get past it on my own…it never seemed to work. At some point in life I got tired. Tired of letting fear paralyze me, hold me in place, and cause me to dismiss God's voice, God's forgiveness, and God's amazing love.

One day in tears, I cried out to God and said, "Lord, help me! The weight and cost of fear is too heavy and too costly. I cannot do this on my own. Please release me of the hold that fear has on my life." God responded back and said, "Faith!" I remember saying, "Lord, please repeat what You just said." He said, "Faith." The force of faith in God will remove the hold that fear has on you.

The contents of this journal are the journey that God took me on. He told me that I had to accept responsibility, establish lessons learned, develop with Him a Plan B, and with the force of faith try again! As you walk through the chapters of this journal, your intentionality of engaging with God, praying, and being honest with yourself will move you to a place and a state of being you have always longed for and are now ready to be at. It is time to accept responsibility.

A Greater Force Than Failure journal by itself is *not* a miracle worker. It is a supplemental vitamin of sorts to your daily self-care regime. You still have to do the work. Get out of your comfort zone. The realm of average or mediocre is not where you dwell. You are a water walker created in God's image to shine brightly to the world. Let your God-given force of faith move you out of your comfort zone. This is your journal. This is your guide. You are ready!

LET'S GO!

ACCEPT RESPONSIBILITY

Taking responsibility for oneself is by definition an act of kindness. – Sharon Salzberg

Accept Responsibility—Holding yourself accountable and responsible for your own conscience decisions is life giving. God implants within you freedom and clarity as you are honest and responsible with the relationship between what you need and what you want. Your "Why" and your "How" are birthed from your conscious acknowledgement of owning your motives and your desired end result.

Remember, you get to choose what path you will walk in. Faith and failure are a choice and a mindset, not a state of being. Regardless of WHY, you made decisions based on a pre-conceived notion that there would be something of benefit to you in the aftermath of your choice.

When you make a choice that does not work out the way you thought it would, own up to it. You are not being kind to yourself or anyone else when you do not take ownership for your own choices. You are actually being irresponsible. Commit your ways and decision to the Lord. Be responsible.

On Proverbs 16:2 NASB

"All the ways of a man are clean in his own sight, but the Lord weighs the motives."

If you're not moving forward, you're falling back.
– Sam Waterston

Read the Key Verse

"To humans belong the plans of the heart, but from the Lord comes the proper answer of the tongue. All a person's ways seem pure to them, but motives are weighed by the Lord. Commit to the Lord whatever you do, and He will establish your plans."
- Proverbs 16:1-3 NIV

REFLECT

What word or idea stuck with you in the key verse?
Write it here, and add why it stuck out:

The moment you take responsibility for everything in your life is the moment you can change anything in your life.
–Hal Elrod

*What is something God is prompting me to do after reading
and reflecting on this Scripture?*

*"Therefore, I tell you, whatever you ask for in prayer, believe that
you have received it, and it will be yours."*
- Mark 11:24 NIV

What does it mean to me to accept responsibility?

Let us move forward with strong and active faith.
–Franklin D. Roosevelt

REFLECT

"But when you ask, you must believe and not doubt, because the one who doubts is like a wave of the sea, blown and tossed by the wind."

- James 1:6 NIV

REFLECT

It is hard for me to be honest with myself because:

"I have chosen the way of faithfulness;
I have set my heart on Your laws."
- Psalm 119:30 NIV

Growing up I never received:

Growing up I always received

"Because you know that the testing of your faith produces perseverance.
- James 1:3 *NIV*

REFLECT

These are the areas of inauthenticity in my life:

Life is 10% what happens to me and 90% how I react to it.
– Charles R. Swindoll

REFLECT

"In my distress I called to the LORD, and He answered me."
- Psalm 120:1 ESV

REFLECT

These are the freedoms
I value in accepting responsibility for all of my decisions:

The hardest part about moving forward is not looking back.
– Anonymous

REFLECT

List what you are willing to sacrifice in order to experience freedom in accepting responsibility for your decisions:

"You make known to me the path of life; in your presence there is fullness of joy; at your right hand are pleasures forevermore."
- Psalm 16:11

STEPS TO LIVING IN FREEDOM

Live in the moment.
Face your fears.
Pray and surrender.

There are two primary choices in life: to accept conditions as they exist or accept the responsibility for changing them
- Dennis Waitley

MEDITATE ON THESE SCRIPTURES

*"In Him and through faith in
Him we may approach God with freedom and confidence."*
- Ephesians 3:12 NIV

*"I will walk about in freedom,
for I have sought out Your precepts."*
- Psalm 119:45 NIV

*"The Spirit of the Lord is on me, because He has anointed me
to proclaim good news to the poor. He has sent me to proclaim
freedom for the prisoners and recovery of sight for the blind,
to set the oppressed free."*
- Luke 4:18 NIV

"So if the Son sets you free, you will be free indeed."
- John 8:36 NIV

Action springs not from thought,
but from a readiness for responsibility.
–Dietrich Bonhoeffer

REFLECT

Acknowledge that you have "blind spots."
What are your personal blind spots?

"Then Jesus declared, I am the bread of life. Whoever comes to Me
will never go hungry, and whoever believes in
Me will never be thirsty."
John 6:35 NIV

REFLECT

Honestly assess your motives, both good and bad.
Commit to staying honest with yourself
and others as you make decisions.

When you choose freedom, you also choose responsibility.
–Richie Norton

Write a personal prayer for the freedom to accept responsibility for your decisions. Prayer is just a conversation with God. Prayers can include worship, confession, thanksgiving and/or requests.

~Believe that God hears and will answer you
-Adrienne Benton

REFLECT

Today I received:

Responsibility is a grace you give yourself not an obligation.
–Dan Millman

REFLECT

Today I reject the thought:

> *"Trust in the Lord with all your heart, and do not lean on your own understanding. In all your ways acknowledge Him, and He will make straight your ways."*
> - Proverbs 3:5-6 ESV

REFLECT

Today God whispered to me:

The time is always right to do what is right.
–Martin Luther King, Jr.

Here are my faith affirmations: List what affirmations you will repeat to yourself and with God's leading, commit to daily. Include Scripture verses that you lean on.

I AM...

"The apostles said to the Lord, 'Increase our faith!"
- Luke 17:5 ESV

REFLECT

You must take personal responsibility. You cannot change the circumstances, the seasons, or the wind, but you can change yourself. That is something you have charge of.
—Jim Rohn

REFLECT

"The plans of the diligent lead surely to advantage, but everyone who is hasty comes surely to poverty."
- Proverbs 21:5 NAS

REFLECT

The key is taking responsibility and initiative, deciding what your life is about, and prioritizing your life around the most important things.
— Stephen Covey

ESTABLISH LESSONS LEARNED

Ultimately there is no such thing as failure. There are lessons learned in different ways.
-Twyla Tharp

TELL THE STORY

I was raised by my parents to be responsible. Throughout my life I have taken great pains to do my utmost to be organized and consistent. When I have failed or had a temporary lapse of judgement, I would take it deeply and hold on to the negative emotions. I would internalize, rest and abide with the pain. One day, I was sharing with a wise mentor and she told me, "Adrienne, you're carrying around weights from your past that are not serving you well. Consider letting them go and most importantly, learn from them and do different. Otherwise, you are bound to repeat the same mistakes." Whew! She was right and I knew it. Pay attention to detail, discern what is holding you back, determine to do different and press toward the goal of living life with purpose.

Fast forward, two year later, I was the Master of Ceremonies for an event. It was time to introduce the keynote speaker. I stepped to the microphone and in that moment, I was suddenly paralyzed. Stricken with embarrassment, gripped by my own sense of judgment. I mean, how could I? He had literally just told me how to properly pronounce his name. I had heard him and in a flash of a moment I could not remember and said it oh so WRONG!!! Oh No…I tried to quickly do damage control and move positively through the awkward moment, but it was too late. The smoke screen was gone, and it was clear to all that I had not properly prepared. I had not taken the time to do my homework and as result I tried to overcompensate and fell flat. Later, as I processed the moment, I asked myself,

"Adrienne, what did you learn from that situation, from that blunder, from that unintentional mistake?" I learned that I have to pay attention to detail. I should have gone over the bulletin, noted that I was unsure of the correct pronunciation and asked him how to correctly pronounce his name instead of deciding to wing it. Lesson learned.

What can you learn from the mistakes that most certainly have taken place in your life? Whether the occurrence is permanently life critical or temporarily momentary, we can learn valuable lessons. Whenever a mistake is made, it is always a moment for course correction. In order to correct and move on smartly, we must first identify what did not work. What was the mistake? Was it truly unintentional? Could it have been avoided?

Keep a record (make mental notes or log in a journal) of the lessons learned so that you are not bound to repeat the same mistakes.

"For we walk by faith, not by sight."
- 2 Corinthians 5:7 NKJ

"My grace is sufficient for you, for My strength is made perfect in weakness. Therefore, most gladly I will rather boast in my infirmities, that the power of Christ may rest upon me."
- 2 Corinthians 12:9 NKJV

*Success is most often achieved
by those who don't know that failure is inevitable.*
- Coco Chanel

REFLECT

What word or idea stuck with you in the key verse?
Write it here, and add why it caught your attention:

"And He said to them, Why are you afraid?
Do you still have no faith?"
- Mark 4:40 NASB

What is something God might be prompting you to do after reading and reflecting on this Scripture?

"If you believe, you will receive whatever you ask for in prayer."
- Matthew 21:22 NIV

REFLECT

*What does it mean to you to establish lessons
learned from past/current mistakes?*

There's an important difference between giving up and letting go.
–Jessica Hatchigan

REFLECT

*It is hard for me to be kind to myself
when I make a mistake because:*

REFLECT

What keeps me from learning from my mistakes?

True peace comes from knowing that God is in control.
– Anonymous

REFLECT

*It is hard for me to find valuable lessons (things I can learn)
from the mistakes I make because:*

*"So faith comes from hearing,
and hearing through the word of Christ."*
- Romans 10:17 ESV

REFLECT

Growing up, this is how I was treated when I made a mistake:

When life seems hopeless, rearrange things for a dose of dopeness.
– Kid Cudi

REFLECT

It is hard for me to receive love. If yes, write down why. Yes or No? Why or Why Not?

"Let your steadfast love, O Lord, be upon us, even as we hope in you."
- Psalm 33:22 ESV

REFLECT

When I make mistakes,
this is how I see myself (describe yourself in the moment):

Feed your fears and your faith will starve.
Feed your faith, and your fears will starve.
–Max Lucado

REFLECT

*"I have fought the good fight, I have finished the race,
I have kept the faith."*
- 2 Timothy 4:7 NIV

REFLECT

This is the freedom
I believe learning from my mistakes will give me:

Sooner or later we've all got to let go of our past.
– Dan Brown

REFLECT

*List what you are willing to sacrifice in order
to learn life lessons from your mistakes:*

*"Therefore, my heart is glad, and my whole being rejoices;
my flesh also dwells secure."*
- Psalm 16:9 ESV

LEARN FROM YOUR MISTAKES

1) Acknowledge your mistakes.

2) Have compassion for yourself.

3) Ask yourself the hard questions.

4) Change your mindset.

5) Create a plan.

6) Make it difficult to mess up.

7) Teach other people.

Meditate on these Scriptures.

"Desire without knowledge is not good and whoever makes haste with his feet misses his way." - Proverbs 19:2 ESV

"He is on the path of life who heeds instruction, but he who forsakes reproof goes astray." - Proverbs 10:17 NASB

"But You, O Lord, are a God merciful and gracious, slow to anger and abounding in steadfast love and faithfulness."
- Psalm 86:15 ESV

REFLECTIONS

1) Look for patterns of behavior–triggers.
List the behaviors/mindset that have kept you stuck in the past.

Immediately the boy's father cried out and said,
"I do believe; help my unbelief."
- Mark 9:24 NASB

2) How will I handle life when
I do not see any clear lessons to learn?

3) How will I rely on God's wisdom as
I learn life lessons from my mistakes?

Faith is like WiFi. It's invisible,
but it has the power to connect you to what you need.
– Anonymous

Write a personal prayer for the power of God to learn lessons from your mistakes. Prayer is just a conversation with God. Prayers can include worship, confession, thanksgiving and/or requests.

- Believe that God hears and will answer you
- Adrienne Benton

REFLECT

"Fear not, for I am with you; be not dismayed, for I am your God;
I will strengthen you, I will help you,
I will uphold you with my righteous right hand."
- Isaiah 41:10 ESV

REFLECT

Today I reject the thought:

Keep faith. The most amazing things in life tend to happen right at the moment you're about to give up hope.

– Anonymous

Today God whispered to me:

"Immediately the boy's father exclaimed, 'I do believe; help me overcome my unbelief!'"
- Mark 9:24 NIV

REFLECT

Here are my faith affirmations: List what affirmations you will repeat to yourself and with God's leading, commit to daily. Include Scripture verses that you lean on.

I AM...

Sometimes the best thing you can do is not think, not wonder, not imagine, not obsess. Just breathe and have faith that everything will work out for the best.

– Anonymous

REFLECT

My personal thoughts:

"Rejoice in hope, be patient in tribulation, be constant in prayer."
- Romans 12:12 ESV

REFLECT

My personal thoughts:

Our anxiety does not empty tomorrow of its sorrows, but only empties today of its strength.

– Charles H. Spurgeon

REFLECT

"And hope does not put us to shame, because God's love has been poured out into our hearts through the Holy Spirit, who has been given to us."
- Romans 5:5 NIV

REFLECT

None of us knows what might happen even the next minute, yet still we go forward. Because we trust. Because we have Faith.
– Paulo Coelho

MOVE FORWARD WITH GOD'S FAITH-FILLED PLAN B

It is now time to faithfully put Plan B in motion. Now that you have looked at what didn't work, explore what will work with God's wisdom leading you.

After the incident where I felt embarrassed because I incorrectly said the name of a guest presenter at a conference, I took the time to reflect on what were the lessons I could possibly learn. I quickly saw that paying attention to detail is vital. I could have taken the time to ask for the correct pronunciation prior to the start of the program. If it was difficult to say correctly, I could have written it down phonetically to make sure that I was respectful to the guest speaker.

Why was this reflection important? I needed to remove myself from negative perceptions from others and myself. I had to create and maintain space in and through my life that God would use and be glorified.

I decided to renew my commitment to myself and pay attention to details. To stop procrastinating. To treat others with respect as I would want to be treated. Sounds easy, but in the grand scheme of life, it can be challenging to maintain our commitment to goodness.

How do you recover when you make a mistake? Mistakes that are light and momentary and mistakes that are costly? Remember, failures provide excellent feedback. Missteps are opportunities for course correction. They can serve the purpose of vital, life-giving redirection.

The faith-filled journey of Plan B requires me to turn to God and commit to ask Him to fill my heart, mind, and soul with His voice, His peace, His strength, and His wisdom. To take my mind and cause me not to procrastinate and to see that I am valued and loved beyond measure. I can get back up and keep on moving forward. Lord, we need you.

Remember, nothing is impossible. What mistake or misstep are you wrestling with today? God wants to move you forward with His faith-filled proactive Plan B. There is nothing, no failure, no mistake you can't recover from. God is waiting for you to turn your eyes, ears, heart, and whole being to Him so He can share with you the faith-filled Plan B for your life. Are you listening?

Read the Key Verse.

"Dear brothers and sisters, when troubles of any kind come your way, consider it an opportunity for great joy. For you know that when your faith is tested, your endurance has a chance to grow. So let it grow, for when your endurance is fully developed, you will be perfect and complete, needing nothing."
- James 1:2-4 NLT

REFLECT

What word or idea stuck with you in the key verse?
Write it here, and add why it stuck out:

Faith and prayer are the vitamins of the soul;
man cannot live in health without them.
—Mahalia Jackson

"Be on your guard; Stand firm in the faith;
be courageous; be strong."
- 1 Corinthians 16:13 NIV

What does it mean to me to have the courage to embark on a faith-filled Plan B after making a mistake or misstep?

A bridge can still be built,
while the bitter waters are flowing beneath.
– Anthony Liccione

REFLECT

*What keeps me from courageously moving forward
and not holding on to past mistakes?*

*"For it is with your heart that you believe and are justified, and it
is with your mouth that you profess your faith and are saved."*
- Romans 10:10 NIV

REFLECT

In the past I have not always chosen to move forward from my mistakes because: (Is there anyone or an experience that you blame for the choices you make/made?)

To let go is to release the images and emotions, the grudges and fears, the clingings and disappointments of the past that bind our spirit.
—Jack Kornfield

*These are my perceived impossibilities/obstacles
for walking a faith-filled life:*

"And by faith even Sarah, who was past childbearing age, was enabled to bear children because she considered Him faithful who had made the promise."
- Hebrews 11:11 NIV

REFLECT

I want to reaffirm faith as a central role in God raising my faith over my fears/insecurities.
(Write Yes and a personal declaration.)

Only when faith replaces doubt in the life of a believer can the joy of knowing God become a reality!
- James MacDonald

Whom would you call a personal hero in your life? Why? How does this your admiration/respect of them challenge, encourage, and clarify your own faith?

"Therefore encourage one another and build one another up, just as you are doing."
- 1 Thessalonians 5:11 ESV

What feelings do you struggle with
when you try to exercise your faith?

The measure of who we are is what we do with what we have.
– Vince Lombardi

REFLECT

What role does God's Word play in your day-to-day faith journey?

"If any of you lacks wisdom, you should ask God, who gives
generously to all without finding fault,
and it will be given to you."
- James 1:5 NIV

REFLECT

How does God know that you trust Him?

Faith is not a part of the Christian life…it's the whole thing.
– James MacDonald

REFLECT

"I hereby command you: Be strong and courageous; do not be frightened or dismayed, for the Lord your God is with you wherever you go."
- Joshua 1:9 NRSV

PLAN B - LIVE OUT YOUR FAITH

Commit your faith walk to the Lord.

Confess your faith with your words and the WORD of God.

Corner your faith with trusting action.

Meditate on these Scriptures.

"No, in all these things we are more than conquerors through Him who loved us."
- Romans 8:37 NIV

"You, dear children, are from God and have overcome them, because the One who is in you is greater than the one who is in the world." - 1 John 4:4 NIV

"Trust in the LORD with all your heart and lean not on your own understanding; in all your ways submit to Him, and He will make your paths straight." - Proverbs 3:5-6 NIV

«Behold, God is my salvation; I will trust, and will not be afraid; for the Lord God is my strength and my song, and he has become my salvation." - Isaiah 12:2 NLT

Don't think you are the "exception" to the rule.

Remember that God's way is the best way.

God stands ready to manifest Plan B for you.

Focus on what matters and let go of what doesn't.
– Unknown

Write a personal prayer for the power of God to lead you on an explosive faith-filled journey. Prayer is just a conversation with God. Prayers can include worship, confession, thanksgiving, and/or requests.

- Believe that God hears and will answer your prayers.
- Adrienne Benton

REFLECT

Today I received:

"*I lift up my eyes to the hills. From where does my help come? My help comes from the LORD, who made heaven and earth.*"
- Psalm 121:1-2 ESV

REFLECT

Today I reject the thought:

Once you accept that perfection is just a goal, screwing up isn't so hard to handle. Each misstep is still a step, another lesson learned, another opportunity to get it right the next time.

– Nick Vujicic

REFLECT

Today God whispered to me:

"Therefore do not be anxious about tomorrow, for tomorrow will be anxious for itself Sufficient for the day is its own trouble."
- Matthew 6:34 ESV

REFLECT

Here are my faith affirmations: List the affirmations you will repeat to yourself and with God's leading, commit to daily. Include Scripture verses that you lean on.

I AM...

Things that will make you unstoppable; Get the naysayers out of your life, Take charge of your destiny, Be uncommon, Be relentless, and Never look backwards.

– Germany Kent

REFLECT

*"The Lord is my strength and my song;
he has become my salvation."*

- Psalm 118:14 ESV

My personal thoughts:

Do not confuse failures with defeat when trying, only recognize what it taught you for the next round.

– Jesus Apolinaris

REFLECT

"When I am afraid, I put my trust in You."
- Psalm 56:3 NIV

TRY AGAIN

Our greatest glory is not in never falling, but in rising up every time we fall.- Confucius

Faith is the foundation, the platform, the firm landing that we stand on every day of our lives. Through the power of God, faith is greater than any obstacle, including the barrier called FEAR. One acronym for fear is False Evidence Appearing Real. The enemy always wants you and I to focus on our fears and not our faith. Remember you are not your mistake. Your previous poor decisions are not your identity. Your misstep was an occurrence, a behavior, a spoken word, but it is not your character, your value system, nor your identity unless you accept it as such.

As we confirm our faith through the Word of God and keep it in our hearts, God is able to activate His promises to us and deliver us so we are empowered to be more than a conqueror. To live our best lives on purpose! Go where we are ordained to go, be who we are ordained by God to be, and let Him manifest His will, His plan, His ordained desires for our lives.

God always wants to do for us more than we could ever think or imagine. Your failures, mistakes, and missteps will never have the power to destroy, derail, or distract you when you place your will in God's hands and ask Him in faith to increase your faith. Proverbs 16:3 says, "Commit your works to the Lord and your thoughts will be established." I can tell you from personal experience, when you trust and try God, He will renew your life and expand your territory and impact for God in way and places you could never have imagined.

God is your biggest fan. He said when you are overwhelmed with fear, remember 2 Tim 1:7 "For the Spirit God gave us does not make us timid, but gives us power, love, and self-discipline." You will never succeed, you will never be transformed, and you will never be free if you don't take that first step again. Sometimes you will have to take it again and again.

Now that God has revealed to you that He wants to conquer your fears and move you forward, it's time TRY AGAIN!

"You have turned for me my mourning into dancing; you have loosed my sackcloth and clothed me with gladness,"
- Psalm 30:11 ESV

REFLECT

What is something God might want you to do after reading and reflecting on this Scripture?

You've gotta know when it's time to turn the page.
– Tori Amos

What does it look like for me to live a faith-filled life day-to-day?

"Go,' said Jesus, 'your faith has healed you.' Immediately he received his sight and followed Jesus along the road."
- Mark 10:52 NIV

REFLECT

I believe God wants me to...
(How is God calling you to engage with Him daily?)

The truth is, unless you let go, unless you forgive yourself, unless you forgive the situation, unless you realize that the situation is over, you cannot move forward.

– Dr. Steve Maraboli

REFLECT

In the past, I have not always chosen to move forward from my mistakes because: (Is there anyone or an experience that you blame for the choices you make/made?)

"But you, man of God, flee from all this, and pursue righteousness, godliness, faith, love, endurance, and gentleness."
- 1 Timothy 6:11 NIV

REFLECT

What does it look like for me to live a faith-filled life day-to-day?

I must give you this warning: your journeys will rarely ever go as you plan. You will make mistakes, and you will feel lost. Whenever that happens, look to the light and keep moving forward in faith.

– Seth Adam Smith

REFLECT

"In the same way, faith by itself,
if it is not accompanied by action, is dead."
- James 2:17 NIV

REFLECT

Describe how you feel about practicing a consistent life of faith.

Don't dwell on what went wrong. Instead, focus on what to do next. Spend your energies on moving forward toward finding the answer.
— Denis Waitley

REFLECT

What area of your life are you experiencing the most tension between practicing faith and canceling your fears?

"As Scripture says,
'Anyone who believes in Him will never be put to shame."
- Romans 10:11 NIV

REFLECT

"We ought always to thank God for you, brothers and sisters, and rightly so, because your faith is growing more and more, and the love all of you have for one another is increasing."
- 2 Thessalonians 1:3 NIV

REFLECT

Describe how you feel about practicing a consistent life of faith?

Life keeps throwing me stones. And I keep finding the diamonds
- Ana Claudia Antunes

REFLECT

What area of your life are you experiencing the most tension between practicing faith and canceling your fears?

"So also you have sorrow now, but I will see you again, and your hearts will rejoice, and no one will take your joy from you."
- John 16:22 ESV

REFLECT

Show me someone who has done something worthwhile, and I'll show you someone who has overcome adversity.
– Lou Holtz

REFLECT

I want to reaffirm faith as a central role
in God raising my faith over my fears/insecurities:
(Write Yes and then a personal declaration.)

"Why are you cast down, O my soul, and why are you in turmoil
within me? Hope in God; for I shall again praise Him,
my salvation and my God."
- Psalm 43:5 ESV

TRY AGAIN

Pray—seek God's guidance.

Pause—get focused.

Pivot—transform your actions from fearful to faithful.

Meditate on these Scriptures.

"But thanks be to God!
He gives us the victory through our Lord Jesus Christ."
- 1 Corinthians 15:57 NIV

"May the God of hope fill you with all joy and peace in believing,
so that by the power of the Holy Spirit you may abound in hope."
- Romans 15:13 ESV

"Be strong and courageous. Do not fear or be in dread of them, for
it is the Lord your God who goes with you.
He will not leave you or forsake you."
- Deuteronomy 31:6 ESV

"And Jesus said to him, 'If you can!'
All things are possible for one who believes."
- Mark 9:23 ESV

REFLECTIONS

"For the Scripture says,
"Whoever believes in him will not be disappointed."
- Romans 10:11 NASB

Only when faith replaces doubt in the life of a believer can the joy of knowing God become a reality!
– James MacDonald

Write a personal prayer for the power of God to lead you on an explosive faith-filled journey. Prayer is just a conversation with God. Prayers can include worship, confession, thanksgiving and/or requests.

- Believe that God hears and will answer your prayers.
- Adrienne Benton

REFLECT

Today I received:

"Behold, the eye of the Lord is on those who fear Him, on those who hope in His steadfast love."
- Psalm 33:18 ESV

REFLECT

Today I reject the thought:

A step from the past always demands a step in the mind backed by a robust action. The very place you fall is the very place you make the first move to move.

– Ernest Agyemang Yeboah

REFLECT

Today God whispered to me:

"Remembering before our God and Father your work of faith and labor of love and steadfastness of hope in our Lord Jesus Christ."
- 1 Thessalonians 1:3 ESV

REFLECT

Here are my faith affirmations: List what affirmations you will repeat to yourself and with God's leading, commit to daily. Include Scripture verses that you lean on.

I AM...

When a caterpillar bursts from its cocoon and discovers it has wings, it does not sit idly, hoping to one day turn back. It flies.
— Kelseyleigh Reber

REFLECT

My personal thoughts:

"But as for me, I will look to the Lord; I will wait for the God of my salvation; my God will hear me."
- Micah 7:7 ESV

REFLECT

My personal thoughts:

Success is the only possible outcome
when one vows to never stop moving forward.
– Edmond Mbiaka

REFLECT

"Know that wisdom is such to your soul; if you find it, there will be a future, and your hope will not be cut off."
- Proverbs 24:14 ESV

COMMITMENT TO
FAITH OVER FEAR

1. Make commitments that are in alignment with God, your purpose, vision, and values. Doing so will ensure that God is leading you and that you will be intentional about your commitment and have a true internal desire to let your faith overrule your fears.

2. Only make commitments that you can deliver on. Don't set yourself up for failure from the start. Be reasonable with yourself and stand on what God shares given your schedule, passion, and needs. Learning to say "No" or "That is not for me" when appropriate is a necessary part of the process of keeping commitments.

3. Document your commitments to writing. Capture your commitment to let God cause your faith to rise daily. Document your faith journey and see the areas you must continuously keep in God's hands and the areas of celebration as you watch God deliver you. Even after you finish this journal, capture your commitments by writing them down.

4. Verbally share your commitments with an accountability partner. Ask someone to come alongside you and hold you accountable. "Two people are better off than one, for they can help each other succeed." Ecclesiastes 4:9 NLT

5. Pray. Pray first, in the middle, and at the end. God will enable you to hold fast to your commitments as you stay in relationship with Him. Pray, "Lord, help me to keep my commitments to my commitments."

REFLECT

How will you live out your commitment to intentionally place your faith over fears?

"Commit your way to the Lord, trust in Him, and He will act."
- Psalm 37:5 ESV

REFLECT

Write a letter to yourself. Affirm what you value about your journey. Confirm how you will move forward with God as your greater force over Failure.

Mobilize forward with God, the greater force than failure as your guide! Let's Go!
- Adrienne Benton

About the Author

Adrienne Townsend Benton

International speaker, trainer, and facilitator, Chaplain Townsend Benton, is in awe of God, who has called her to non-traditional ministry to show how Christ is real and relevant to people's everyday living needs. Chaplain Benton holds an A.S. in Early Childhood, B.A. in Elementary Education and Psychology, MA in Curriculum and Instruction, and the Master of Divinity degree from the Seventh-day Adventist Theological Seminary at Andrews University. Chaplain Townsend Benton served as an Associate Dean of Women on the campus of Andrews University and as an associate minister on the pastoral staff of Andrews University's New Life Seventh-day-Adventist Fellowship. Adrienne and her husband Theron reside in

Summerville, SC, and revel in the opportunity to bring hope and the light of Christ to precious souls in the dark corners of life is a mission that I am privileged to embrace daily.